The Book OF COMPLETE
NONSENSE

VINTAGE BOOKS
London

Published by Vintage 2013

2 4 6 8 10 9 7 5 3 1

Vintage
Random House, 20 Vauxhall Bridge Road,
London SW1V 2SA

www.vintage-classics.info

Addresses for companies within The Random House Group Limited can be found at:
www.randomhouse.co.uk/offices.htm

The Random House Group Limited Reg. No. 954009

A CIP catalogue record for this book
is available from the British Library

ISBN 9780099582663

The Random House Group Limited supports The Forest Stewardship Council® (FSC®),
the leading international forest certification organisation. Our books carrying the FSC
label are printed on FSC®-certified paper. FSC is the only forest certification scheme
supported by the leading environmental organisations, including Greenpeace. Our
paper procurement policy can be found at www.randomhouse.co.uk/environment

Typeset by Palimpsest Book Production Limited,
Falkirk, Stirlingshire
Printed and bound in Great Britain by
CPI Group (UK) Ltd, Croydon CR0 4YY

CONTENTS

A Little Limerickical Interlude

The Utter Zoo Alphabet

Edward Gorey

The Amphoo is intensely neat;
Its head is small, likewise its feet.

The Boggerslosh conceals itself
In back of bottles on a shelf.

The Crunk is not unseldom drastic
And must be hindered by elastic.

The Dawbis is remote and shy;
It shuns the gaze of passers-by.

The Epitwee's inclined to fits
Until at last it falls to bits.

The Fidknop is devoid of feeling;
It drifts about beneath the ceiling.

The Gawdge is understood to save
All sorts of objects in its cave.

The Humglum crawls along the ground,
And never makes the slightest sound.

The Ippagoggy has a taste
For every kind of glue and paste.

The Jelbislup cannot get far
Because it's kept inside a jar.

The Kwongdzu has enormous claws;
Its character is full of flaws.

The Limpflig finds it hard to keep
From spending all its life asleep.

The Mork proceeds with pensive grace
And no expression on its face.

The Neapse's sufferings are chronic;
It lives exclusively on tonic.

The Ombledroom is vast and white,
And therefore visible by night.

The Posby goes into a trance
In which it does a little dance.

The Quingawaga squeaks and moans
While dining off of ankle bones.

The Raitch hangs downwards from its tail
By knotting it around a nail.

The Scrug's extremely nasty-looking,
And is unusable for cooking.

The Twibbit on occasion knows
A difficulty with its toes.

The Ulp is very, very small;
It hardly can be seen at all.

The Veazy makes a creaking noise;
It has no dignity or poise.

The Wambulus has floppy ears
With which to wipe away its tears.

The Xyke stands up at close of day,
And then it slowly walks away.

The Yawfle stares, and stares, and stares,
And stares, and stares, and stares, and stares.

About the Zote what can be said?
There was just one, and now it's dead.

Shoem*

Liz Brownlee

Time flizzes when I'm wrizzing –
some words are toomely long,
and so I merge and jummix
to squeet them in my song.

It's really not too diffcky
to get my words to scrush –
saves tromoil and timassle,
when in a hurrid rush.

There's only one small difflem
for my puzzizzy head –
I'm baffplussed and conboozled
by what it is I said!

*Short Poem
Flizzes = flies and whizzes
Toomley = too and extremely
Squeet = squeeze and fit
Scrush = squash and crush
Timassle = time and hassle
Difflem = difficulty and problem
Baffplussed = baffled and
    nonplussed

Wrizzing = busy and writing
Jummix = jumble and mix
Diffcky = difficult and tricky
Tromoil = trouble and turmoil
Hurrid = hurried and horrid
Puzzizzy = puzzled and dizzy
Conboozled = confused and
    bamboozled

4

The Sniffle

Ogden Nash

In spite of her sniffle
Isabel's chiffle.
Some girls with a sniffle
Would be weepy and tiffle;
They would look awful,
Like a rained-on waffle,
But Isabel's chiffle
In spite of her sniffle.
Her nose is more red
With a cold in her head,
But then, to be sure,
Her eyes are bluer.
Some girls with a snuffle,
Their tempers are uffle.
But when Isabel's snivelly
She's snivelly civilly,
And when she's snuffly
She's perfectly luffly.

Lettuce Marry

Anonymous

Do you carrot all for me?
My heart beets for you,
With your turnip nose
And your radish face.
You are a peach.
If we cantaloupe
Lettuce marry;
Weed make a swell pear.

The Land of the Bumbley Boo

Spike Milligan

In the Land of the Bumbley Boo
The people are red white and blue,
They never blow noses,
Or even wear closes,
What a sensible thing to do!

In the Land of the Bumbley Boo
You can buy Lemon pie at the Zoo;
They give away Foxes
In little Pink Boxes
And Bottles of Dandelion Stew.

In the Land of the Bumbley Boo
You never see a Gnu,
But thousands of cats
Wearing trousers and hats
Made of Pumpkins and Pelican Glue!

Chorus
Oh, the Bumbley Boo! the Bumbley Boo!
That's the place for me and you!
So hurry! Let's run!
The train leaves at one!
For the Land of the Bumbley Boo!
The wonderful Bumbley Boo-Boo-Boo!
The wonderful Bumbley BOO!!!

Of Pygmies, Palms and Pirates

Mervyn Peake

Of pygmies, palms and pirates,
Of islands and lagoons,
Of blood-bespotted frigates,
Of crags and octoroons,
Of whales and broken bottles,
Of quicksands cold and grey,
Of ullages and dottles,
I have no more to say.

Of barley, corn and furrows,
Of farms and turf that heaves
Above such ghostly burrows
As twitch on summer eves
Of fallow-land and pasture,
Of skies both pink and grey,
I made my statement last year
And have no more to say.

The Walrus and the Carpenter

Lewis Carroll

The sun was shining on the sea,
　　Shining with all his might:
He did his very best to make
　　The billows smooth and bright –
And this was odd, because it was
　　The middle of the night.

The moon was shining sulkily,
　　Because she thought the sun
Had got no business to be there
　　After the day was done –
'It's very rude of him,' she said,
　　'To come and spoil the fun!'

The sea was wet as wet could be,
　　The sands were dry as dry.
You could not see a cloud, because
　　No cloud was in the sky:
No birds were flying overhead –
　　There were no birds to fly.

The Walrus and the Carpenter
　　Were walking close at hand;

They wept like anything to see
    Such quantities of sand:
'If this were only cleared away,'
    They said, 'it *would* be grand!'

'If seven maids with seven mops
    Swept it for half a year.
Do you suppose,' the Walrus said,
    'That they could get it clear?'
'I doubt it,' said the Carpenter,
    And shed a bitter tear.

'O Oysters, come and walk with us!'
    The Walrus did beseech.
'A pleasant walk, a pleasant talk,
    Along the briny beach:
We cannot do with more than four,
    To give a hand to each.'

The eldest Oyster looked at him,
    But never a word he said:
The eldest Oyster winked his eye,
    And shook his heavy head –
Meaning to say he did not choose
    To leave the oyster-bed.

But four young Oysters hurried up,
    All eager for the treat:

Their coats were brushed, their faces washed,
    Their shoes were clean and neat –
And this was odd, because, you know,
    They hadn't any feet.

Four other Oysters followed them,
    And yet another four;
And thick and fast they came at last,
    And more, and more, and more –
All hopping through the frothy waves,
    And scrambling to the shore.

The Walrus and the Carpenter
    Walked on a mile or so,
And then they rested on a rock
    Conveniently low:
And all the little Oysters stood
    And waited in a row.

'The time has come,' the Walrus said,
    'To talk of many things:
Of shoes – and ships – and sealing-wax –
    Of cabbages – and kings –
And why the sea is boiling hot –
    And whether pigs have wings.'

'But wait a bit,' the Oysters cried,
    'Before we have our chat;

For some of us are out of breath,
	And all of us are fat!'
'No hurry!' said the Carpenter.
	They thanked him much for that.

'A loaf of bread,' the Walrus said,
	'Is what we chiefly need:
Pepper and vinegar besides
	Are very good indeed –
Now if you're ready, Oysters dear,
	We can begin to feed.'

'But not on us!' the Oysters cried,
	Turning a little blue.
'After such kindness, that would be
	A dismal thing to do!'
'The night is fine,' the Walrus said.
	'Do you admire the view?

'It was so kind of you to come!
	And you are very nice!'
The Carpenter said nothing but
	'Cut us another slice:
I wish you were not quite so deaf –
	I've had to ask you twice!'

'It seems a shame,' the Walrus said,
	'To play them such a trick,

After we've brought them out so far,
    And made them trot so quick!'
The Carpenter said nothing but
    'The butter's spread too thick!'

'I weep for you,' the Walrus said:
    'I deeply sympathize.'
With sobs and tears he sorted out
    Those of the largest size,
Holding his pocket-handkerchief
    Before his streaming eyes.

'O Oysters,' said the Carpenter,
    'You've had a pleasant run!
Shall we be trotting home again?'
    But answer came there none –
And this was scarcely odd, because
    They'd eaten every one.

'Tis Midnight

Anonymous

'Tis midnight, and the setting sun
    Is slowly rising in the west;
The rapid rivers slowly run,
    The frog is on his downy nest.
The pensive goat and sportive cow
    Hilarious, leap from bough to bough.

One Fine Day in the Middle of the Night

Anonymous

One fine day in the middle of the night,
Two dead men got up to fight,
Back to back they faced each other,
Drew their swords and shot each other.

Calico Pie

Edward Lear

Calico Pie,
  The little Birds f l y
Down to the calico tree,
  Their wings were blue,
  And they sang 'Tilly-loo!'
  Till away they flew, –
And they never came back to me!
  They never came back!
  They never came back!
They never came back to me!

  Calico Jam,
  The little Fish s w a m ,
Over the syllabub sea,
  He took off his hat,
  To the Sole and the Sprat,
  And the Willeby-Wat, –
But he never came back to me!
  He never came back!
  He never came back!
He never came back to me!

        Calico Ban,
    The little Mice r a n,
To be ready in time for tea,
    Flippity flup,
    They drank it all up,
    And danced in the cup, –
But they never came back to me!
    They never came back!
    They never came back!
They never came back to me!

        Calico Drum,
    The Grasshoppers come,
The Butterfly, Beetle, and Bee,
    Over the ground,
    Around and around,

    With a ♭ᵒp and a bᵒund, –

But they never came back!
    They never came back!
    They never came back!
They never came back to me!

On the Ning Nang Nong

Spike Milligan

On the Ning Nang Nong
Where the Cows go Bong!
And the Monkeys all say Boo!
There's a Nong Nang Ning
Where the trees go Ping!
And the tea pots Jibber Jabber Joo.
On the Nong Ning Nang
All the mice go Clang!
And you just can't catch 'em when they do!
So it's Ning Nang Nong!
Cows go Bong!
Nong Nang Ning!
Trees go Ping!
Nong Ning Nang!
The mice go Clang!
What a noisy place to belong,
Is the Ning Nang Ning Nang Nong!

As I Was Going Out One Day

Anonymous

As I was going out one day
My head fell off and rolled away,
But when I saw that it was gone,
I picked it up and put it on.

And when I got into the street
A fellow cried 'Look at your feet!'
I looked at them and sadly said
'I've left them both asleep in bed!'

There Was an Old Man on Some Rocks

Edward Lear

There was an old man on some rocks,
Who shut his wife up in a box;
　　When she said, 'Let me out!'
　　He exclaimed, 'Without doubt,
You will pass all your life in that box.'

Solomon Grundy

Anonymous

Solomon Grundy,
Born on Monday,
Christened on Tuesday,
Married on Wednesday,
Took ill on Thursday,
Worse on Friday,
Died on Saturday,
Buried on Sunday,
This is the end
Of Solomon Grundy.

There Was an Old Man Named Michael Finnigin

Anonymous

There was an old man named Michael Finnigin
He grew whiskers on his chinnigin
The wind came out and blew them innigin
Poor old Michael Finnigin, beginnigin

There was an old man named Michael Finnigin
He went fishing with a pinnigin
Caught a fish and dropped
    it innigin
Poor old Michael Finnigin,
    beginnigin

There was an old man named Michael Finnigin
Climbed a tree and hurt
    his shinnigin
Took off several yards
    of skinnigin
Poor old Michael Finnigin,
    beginnigin

There was an old man named Michael Finnigin
He got drunk from too much ginnigin
So he wasted all this tinnigin
Poor old Michael Finnigin, beginnigin

There was an old man named Michael Finnigin
He kicked up an awful dinnigin
Because they said he must not sinnigin
Poor old Michael Finngin, beginnigin

There was an old man named Michael Finnigin
He grew fat and he grew thinnigin
Then he died, and we have to beginnigin
Poor old Michael Finnigin, beginnigin

Father William

Lewis Carroll

'You are old, Father William,' the young man said,
   'And your hair has become very white;
And yet you incessantly stand on your head –
   Do you think, at your age, it is right?'

'In my youth,' Father William replied to his son,
   'I feared it might injure the brain;
But, now that I'm perfectly sure I have none,
   Why, I do it again and again.'

'You are old,' said the youth, 'As I mentioned before,
   And have grown most uncommonly fat;
Yet you turned a back-somersault in at the door –
   Pray, what is the reason of that?'

'In my youth,' said the sage, as he shook his grey locks,
   'I kept all my limbs very supple
By the use of this ointment – one shilling the box –
   Allow me to sell you a couple?'

'You are old,' said the youth, 'And your jaws are too weak
   For anything tougher than suet;

Yet you finished the goose, with the bones and the beak –
    Pray, how did you manage to do it?'

'In my youth,' said his father, 'I took to the law,
    And argued each case with my wife;
And the muscular strength which it gave to my jaw,
    Has lasted the rest of my life.'

'You are old,' said the youth, 'one would hardly suppose
    That your eye was as steady as ever;
Yet you balanced an eel on the end of your nose –
    What made you so awfully clever?'

'I have answered three questions, and that is enough,'
    Said his father; 'don't give yourself airs!
Do you think I can listen all day to such stuff?
    Be off, or I'll kick you down-stairs!'

Do Your Ears Hang Low?

Anonymous

Do your ears hang low?
Do they wobble to and fro?
Can you tie them in a knot?
Can you tie them in a bow?
Can you throw them o'er your shoulder
like a regimental soldier
Do your ears hang low?

Do your ears hang high?
Do they reach up to the sky?
Do they droop when they are wet?
Do they straighten when they're dry?
Can you wave to your neighbour
with a minimum of labour?
Do your ears hang high?

Do your ears flip-flop?
Can you use them as a mop?
Are they stringy at the bottom?
Are they curly at the top?

Can you use them for a swatter?
Can you use them for a blotter?
Do your ears flip-flop?

Do your ears stick out?
Can you waggle them about?
Can you flap them up and down
as you fly around the town?
Can you shut them up for sure
when you hear an awful bore?
Do your ears stick out?

Be Glad Your Nose is on Your Face

Jack Prelutsky

Be glad your nose is on your face,
not pasted on some other place,
for if it were where it is not,
you might dislike your nose a lot.

Imagine if your precious nose
were sandwiched in between your toes,
that clearly would not be a treat,
for you'd be forced to smell your feet.

Your nose would be a source of dread
were it attached atop your head,
it soon would drive you to despair,
forever tickled by your hair.

Within your ear, your nose would be
an absolute catastrophe,
for when you were obliged to sneeze,
your brain would rattle from the breeze.

Your nose, instead, through thick and thin,
remains between your eyes and chin,
not pasted on some other place –
be glad your nose is on your face!

Government Health Warning

Chrissie Gittins

Don't squash peas on your knees,
Don't grate carrot on a parrot,
Don't tangle pears in your nostril hairs
Never risk a quid on a squid.

Don't pour bottled beer in your ear.
Never slice apple pies on your thighs.
Never wash your pullovers with yesterday's leftovers.
Don't entice a bowl of egg fried rice.

Don't assume that tarragon's a paragon,
Or try to run faster than a bag of spinach pasta,
Don't try to lunge at Victoria sponge,
A cake with a steak is a mistake.

Bravado never works with avocado,
A flickin's not the thing to give to chicken,
Don't go and stutter on the b-b-b-b-butter
Never feed mice on ice.

Careful not to ravage a coy savoy cabbage,
Never have a tussle with a mussel,
Don't ever hurry with a spicy prawn curry,
Don't boast about your buttered toast.

Don't pour jelly in your welly,
Don't dribble tagliatelle on your older brother's belly.
Never do the tango with a ripe and juicy mango,
If you do then you're sure to pay the price!

Strict

Michael Rosen

Maybe you think you have a
teacher
who's really strict.
maybe you know a really strict
teacher.
But when I was at school
we had a teacher who was so strict
you weren't allowed to breathe in
her lessons.
That's true, we weren't allowed to breathe.
It was really hard to get through
a whole day without breathing.
Lips tightly shut.
Face going red.
Eyeballs popping out.
She'd go round the class glaring at us
and then she'd suddenly catch sight of
one of us and she'd yell,
'NO BREATHING, DO YOU
HEAR ME? NO BREATHING.'
And you had to stop breathing
right away.
The naughty ones used to try and

take quick secret breaths
under the table.
They'd duck down where she
couldn't see them
snatch a quick breath and come
back up
with their mouth shut tight.
Then someone would say,
'Excuse me, miss, can I go outside
and do some breathing?'
And she'd say,
'WHAT? CAN'T YOU WAIT?
YOU'VE HAD ALL PLAYTIME
TO BREATHE, HAVEN'T YOU?'
And then she'd ask someone a
question
like, 'Where's Tibet?'
and someone'd put up their hand
and say 'Er . . . it's – '
and she'd be right in there with:
'YOU'RE BREATHING. I SAW
YOU BREATHE.'
'I wasn't, miss, really I wasn't.'
'WELL YOU ARE NOW,
AREN'T YOU?'
It was terrible.
She was so strict . . .

You Must Never Bath in an Irish Stew

Spike Milligan

You must never bath in an Irish Stew
It's a most illogical thing to do
   But should you persist against my reasoning
   Don't fail to add the appropriate seasoning.

I Love to Do My Homework

Anonymous

I love to do my homework
I never miss a day
I even love the men in white
Who are taking me away.

The Gardener's Song

Lewis Carroll

He thought he saw an Elephant,
    That practised on a fife:
He looked again, and found it was
    A letter from his wife.
'At length I realise,' he said,
    'The bitterness of Life!'

He thought he saw a Buffalo
    Upon the chimney-piece:
He looked again, and found it was
    His Sister's Husband's Niece.
'Unless you leave this house,' he said,
    'I'll send for the Police!'

He thought he saw a Rattlesnake
    That questioned him in Greek:
He looked again, and found it was
    The Middle of Next Week.
'The one thing I regret,' he said,
    'Is that it cannot speak!'

He thought he saw a Banker's Clerk
Descending from the bus:
He looked again, and found it was
A Hippopotamus.
'If this should stay to dine,' he said,
'There won't be much for us!'

He thought he saw a Kangaroo
That worked a coffee-mill:
He looked again, and found it was
A Vegetable-Pill.
'Were I to swallow this,' he said,
'I should be very ill!'

He thought he saw a Coach-and-Four
That stood beside his bed:
He looked again, and found it was
A Bear without a Head.
'Poor thing,' he said, 'poor silly thing!
It's waiting to be fed!'

He thought he saw an Albatross
That fluttered round the lamp:
He looked again, and found it was
A Penny-Postage Stamp.
'You'd best be getting home,' he said:
'The nights are very damp!'

He thought he saw a Garden-Door
    That opened with a key:
He looked again, and found it was
    A double Rule of Three:
'And all its mystery,' he said,
    'Is clear as day to me!'

He thought he saw a Argument
    That proved he was the Pope:
He looked again, and found it was
    A Bar of Mottled Soap.
'A fact so dread,' he faintly said,
    'Extinguishes all hope!'

Nobody Loves Me

Anonymous

Nobody loves me,
Everybody hates me,
I think I'll go and eat worms.

Big fat squishy ones,
Little thin skinny ones
See how they wriggle and squirm.

Bite their heads off.
'Schlurp!' they're lovely,
Throw their tails away.

Nobody knows
How big I grows
On worms three times a day.

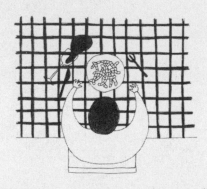

A LITTLE
LIMERICKICAL
INTERLUDE

There Was a Young Lady of Ryde

Anonymous

There was a young lady of Ryde
Who ate a green apple and died;
The apple fermented
Inside the lamented,
And made cider inside her inside.

There Was an Old Man of Dumbree

Edward Lear

There was an old man of Dumbree,
Who taught little owls to drink tea;
For he said, 'To eat mice,
Is not proper or nice'
That amiable man of Dumbree.

There was a Young Lady of Dorking

Edward Lear

There was a young lady of Dorking,
Who bought a large bonnet for walking;
But its colour and size,
So bedazzled her eyes,
That she very soon went back to Dorking.

There Was an Old Man With a Beard

Edward Lear

There was an old man with a beard,
Who said, 'It is just as I feared!
Two Owls and a Hen,
Four Larks and a Wren,
Have all built their nests in my beard!'

There Was a Young Lady Whose Chin

Edward Lear

There was a young lady whose chin,
Resembled the point of a pin;
So she had it made sharp,
And purchased a harp,
And played several tunes with her chin.

There was an Old Man of Kilkenny

Edward Lear

There was an old man of Kilkenny,
Who never had more than a penny;
He spent all that money,
In onions and honey,
That wayward Old Man of Kilkenny.

There Was a Young Lady of Norway

Edward Lear

There was a young lady of Norway,
Who casually sat on a doorway;
When the door squeezed her flat,
She exclaimed, 'What of that?'
This courageous Young Lady of Norway.

There Was an Old Man of Melrose

Edward Lear

There was an old man of Melrose,
Who walked on the tips of his toes;
But they said, 'It ain't pleasant,
To see you at present,
You stupid Old Man of Melrose.'

There Was an Old Lady Whose Folly

Edward Lear

There was an old lady whose folly,
Induced her to sit on a holly;
Whereon by a thorn,
Her dress being torn,
She quickly became melancholy.

There Was an Old Man of The Hague

Edward Lear

There was an old man of The Hague,
Whose ideas were excessively vague;
He built a balloon
To examine the moon,
That deluded Old Man of The Hague.

There Was an Old Lady of Chertsey

Edward Lear

There was an old lady of Chertsey,
Who made a remarkable curtsey;
She twirled round and round,
Till she sunk underground,
Which distressed all the people of Chertsey.

There Was an Old Man of Nepaul

Edward Lear

There was an old man of Nepaul
From his horse had a terrible fall;
But, though split quite in two,
By some very strong glue,
They mended that Man of Nepaul.

There Was a Young Lad of St Just

Anonymous

There was a young lad of St Just
Who ate apple pie till he bust.
It wasn't the fru-it
That caused him to do it,
What finished him off was the crust.

There Once Was a Man

Charles Causley

There once was a man
Called Knocketty Ned
Who wore his cat
On top of his head.
Upstairs, downstairs,
The whole world knew
Wherever he went
The cat went too.

He wore it at work,
He wore it at play,
He wore it to town
On market day,
And for fear it should rain
Or the snowflakes fly
He carried a brolly
To keep it dry.

He never did fret
Nor fume because
He always knew
Just where it was
'And when,' said Ned,

'In my bed I lie
There's no better nightcap
Money can buy.

'There's no better bonnet
To be found,'
Said Knocketty Ned,
'The world around.
And furthermore
Was there ever a hat
As scared a mouse
Or scared a rat?'

Did you ever hear
Of a tale like that
As Knocketty Ned's
And the tale of his cat?

Cabbage

Roger McGough

The cabbage is a funny veg.
All crisp, and green, and brainy.
I sometimes wear one on my head
When it's cold and rainy.

There Was an Old Person Whose Habits

Edward Lear

There was an old person whose habits,
Induced him to feed upon rabbits;
When he'd eaten eighteen,
He turned perfectly green,
Upon which he relinquished those habits.

The Centipede's Song

Roald Dahl

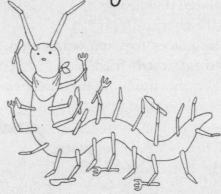

'I've eaten many strange and scrumptious dishes in my
      time,
Like jellied gnats and dandyprats and earwigs cooked
      in slime,
And mice with rice – they're really nice
When roasted in their prime.
(But don't forget to sprinkle them with just a pinch of
      grime.)

'I've eaten fresh mudburgers by the greatest cooks
      there are,
And scrambled dregs and stinkbugs' eggs and hornets
      stewed in tar,
And pails of snails and lizards' tails,
And beetles by the jar.
(A beetle is improved by just a splash of vinegar.)

'I often eat boiled slobbages. They're grand when
     served beside
Minced doodlebugs and curried slugs. And have you
     ever tried
Mosquitoes' toes and wampfish roes
Most delicately fried?
(The only trouble is they disagree with my inside.)

'I'm mad for crispy wasp-stings on a piece of buttered
     toast,
And pickled spines of porcupines. And then a
     gorgeous roast
Of dragon's flesh, well hung, not fresh –
It costs a pound at most,
(And comes to you in barrels if you order it by post.)

'I crave the tasty tentacles of octopi for tea
I like hot-dogs, I LOVE hot-frogs, and surely you'll agree
A plate of soil with engine oil's
A super recipe.
(I hardly need to mention that it's practically free.)

'For dinner on my birthday shall I tell you what I
    chose:
Hot noodles made from poodles on a slice of garden
    hose –
And a rather smelly jelly
Made of armadillo's toes.
(The jelly is delicious, but you have to hold your
    nose.)

'Now comes,' *the Centipede declared,* 'the burden of my
    speech:
These foods are rare beyond compare – some are right
    out of reach;
But there's no doubt I'd go without
A million plates of each
For one small mite,
One tiny bite
Of this FANTASTIC PEACH!'

I Eat My Peas With Honey

Anonymous

I eat my peas with honey;
I've done it all my life.
It makes them taste quite funny,
But it keeps them on the knife.

Crazy Mayonnaisy Mum

Julia Donaldson

When my friends come home with me
They never want to stay to tea
Because of Mum's peculiar meals
Like strawberries with jellied eels.
You should see her lick her lips
And sprinkle sugar on the chips,
Then pass a cup of tea to you
And ask, 'One salt or two?'

Whoops-a-daisy,
That's my crazy
Mayonnaisy mum.

She serves up ice cream with baked beans,
And golden syrup with sardines,
And curried chocolate mousse on toast,
And once she iced the Sunday roast.
When my birthday comes she'll make
A steak and kidney birthday cake.
There'll be jelly too, of course,
With cheese and onion sauce.

Whoops-a-daisy,
That's my crazy
Mayonnaisy mum.

What's she put in my packed lunch?
A bag of rhubarb crisps to crunch.
Lots of sandwiches as well,
But what is in them? Who can tell?
It tastes like marmalade and ham,
Or maybe fish paste mixed with jam.
What's inside my flask today?
Spinach squash – hooray!

Whoops-a-daisy,
That's my crazy
Mayonnaisy mum.

Beautiful Soup

Lewis Carroll

Beautiful Soup, so rich and green,
Waiting in a hot tureen!
Who for such dainties would not stoop?
Soup of the evening, beautiful Soup!
Soup of the evening, beautiful Soup!
Beau – ootiful Soo – oop!
Beau – ootiful Soo – oop!
Soo – oop of the e – e – evening,
Beautiful, beauti-ful Soup?

Beautiful Soup! Who cares for fish,
Game, or any other dish?
Who would not give all else for two
Pennyworth only of Beautiful Soup?
Pennyworth only of Beautiful Soup?
Beau – ootiful Soo – oop!
Beau – ootiful Soo – oop!
Soo – oop of the e – e – evening,
Beautiful, beauti – FUL SOUP!

Sky in the Pie!

Roger McGough

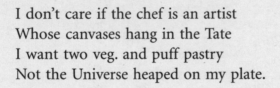

Waiter, there's a sky in my pie
Remove it at once if you please
You can keep your incredible sunsets
I ordered mincemeat and cheese.

I can't stand nightingales singing
Or clouds burnished with gold
The whispering breeze is disturbing
   the peas
And making my chips go all cold.

I don't care if the chef is an artist
Whose canvases hang in the Tate
I want two veg. and puff pastry
Not the Universe heaped on my plate.

OK I'll try just a spoonful
I suppose I've got nothing to lose
Mm . . . the colours quite tickle the palette
With a blend of delicate hues.

The sun has a custardy flavour
And the clouds are as light as air

And the wind a chewier texture,
(With a hint of cinnamon there?)

The sky is simply delicious
Why haven't I tried it before?
I can chew my way through to Eternity
And still have room left for more.

Having acquired a taste for the Cosmos
I'll polish this sunset off soon
I can't wait to tuck into the night sky
Waiter! Please bring me the Moon!

It's Raining Pigs and Noodles

Jack Prelutsky

It's raining pigs and noodles,
it's pouring frogs and hats,
chrysanthemums and poodles,
bananas, brooms and cats.
Assorted prunes and parrots
are dropping from the sky,
here comes a bunch of carrots,
some hippopotami.

It's raining pens and pickles,
and eggs and silverware.
A flood of figs and nickels
is falling through the air.
I see a swan, a sweater,
a clock, a model train –
I like this so much better
than when it's raining rain.

There Once Was a Man of Bengal

Anonymous

There once was a man of Bengal
Who was asked to a fancy dress ball;
He murmured: 'I'll risk it
and go as a biscuit . . .'
But a dog ate him up in the hall.

The Cow

Ogden Nash

The cow is of the bovine ilk;
One end is moo, the other, milk.

Luv Song

Benjamin Zephaniah

I am in luv wid a hedgehog
I've never felt dis way before
I have luv fe dis hedgehog
An everyday I luv her more an more,
She lives by de shed
Where weeds an roses bed
An I just want de world to know
She makes me glow.

I am in luv wid a hedgehog
She's making me hair stand on edge,
So in luv wid dis hedgehog
An her friends
Who all live in de hedge
She visits me late
An eats off Danny's plate
But Danny's a cool tabby cat
He leaves it at dat.

I am in luv wid a hedgehog,
She's gone away so I must wait
But I do miss my hedgehog
Everytime she goes to hibernate.

The Christening

A.A. Milne

What shall I call
    My dear little dormouse?
His eyes are small
    But his tail is e-nor-mouse.

I sometimes call him Terrible John,
'Cos his tail goes on –
And on –
And on.
And I sometimes call him Terrible Jack,
'Cos his tail goes on to the end of his back.
And I sometimes call him Terrible James,
'Cos he says he likes me calling him names . . .
    But I think I shall call him Jim
    'Cos I *am* fond of him!

A Tree Toad Loved a She-Toad

Anonymous

A tree toad loved a she-toad
That lived up a tree.
She was a three-toed tree toad
But a two-toed toad was he.
The two-toed toad tried to win
The three-toed she-toad's friendly nod,
For the two-toed toad loved the ground
On which the three-toed she-toad trod.
But no matter how the two-toed tree toad tried,
He could not please her whim.
From her tree-toad bower,
With her three-toed power
The she-toad vetoed him.

The Owl and the Pussy-Cat

Edward Lear

The Owl and the Pussy-cat went to sea
In a beautiful pea-green boat,
They took some honey, and plenty of money,
Wrapped up in a five-pound note.
The Owl looked up to the stars above,
And sang to a small guitar,
'O lovely Pussy! O Pussy my love,
What a beautiful Pussy you are,
You are,
You are!
What a beautiful Pussy you are!'

Pussy said to the Owl, 'You elegant fowl!
How charmingly sweet you sing!
O let us be married! too long we have tarried:
But what shall we do for a ring?'
They sailed away, for a year and a day,
To the land where the Bong-tree grows
And there in a wood a Piggy-wig stood
With a ring at the end of his nose,
His nose,
His nose,
With a ring at the end of his nose.

'Dear pig, are you willing to sell for one shilling
Your ring?' Said the Piggy, 'I will.'
So they took it away, and were married next day
By the Turkey who lives on the hill.
They dined on mince, and slices of quince,
Which they ate with a runcible spoon;
And hand in hand, on the edge of the sand,
They danced by the light of the moon,
The moon,
The moon,
They danced by the light of the moon.

High Diddle Diddle

Anonymous

High diddle diddle,
The cat and the fiddle,
The cow jump'd over the moon;
The little dog laugh'd
To see such craft,
And the dish ran away with the spoon.

I Saw a Jolly Hunter

Charles Causley

I saw a jolly hunter
With a jolly gun
Walking in the country
In the jolly sun.

In the jolly meadow
Sat a jolly hare.
Saw the jolly hunter.
Took jolly care.

Hunter jolly eager –
Sight of jolly prey.
Forgot gun pointing
Wrong jolly way.

Jolly hunter jolly head
Over heels gone.
Jolly old safety-catch
Not jolly on.

Bang went the jolly gun.
Hunter jolly dead.
Jolly hare got clean away.
Jolly good, I said.

There Was a Crooked Man

Anonymous

There was a crooked man, and he went a crooked mile,

He found a crooked sixpence against a crooked stile:

He bought a crooked cat which caught a crooked
  mouse,

And they all lived together in a little crooked house.

There Was an Old Man of Peru

Edward Lear

There was an old man of Peru,
Who watched his wife making a stew;
But once by mistake,
In a stove she did bake,
That unfortunate Man of Peru.

Algy Met a Bear

Anonymous

Algy met a bear,
a bear met Algy:
the bear grew **bulg**y;
the **bulge** was Algy.

The Adventures of Isabel

Ogden Nash

Isabel met an enormous bear,
Isabel, Isabel, didn't care;
The bear was hungry, the bear was ravenous,
The bear's big mouth was cruel and cavernous.
The bear said, Isabel, glad to meet you,
How do, Isabel, now I'll eat you!
Isabel, Isabel, didn't worry,
Isabel didn't scream or scurry,
She washed her hands and she straightened her hair up,
Then Isabel quietly ate the bear up.

Once in a night as black as pitch
Isabel met a wicked witch.
The witch's face was cross and
    wrinkled,
The witch's gums with teeth were
    sprinkled.
Ho, ho, Isabel! the old witch crowed,
I'll turn you into an ugly toad!
Isabel, Isabel, didn't worry,
Isabel didn't scream or scurry,
She showed no rage, she showed
    no rancor,
But she turned the witch into
    milk and drank her.

Isabel met a hideous giant,
Isabel continued self-reliant.
The giant was hairy, the giant was horrid,
He had one eye in the middle of his forehead.
Good morning, Isabel, the giant said,
I'll grind your bones to make my bread.
Isabel, Isabel, didn't worry,
Isabel didn't scream or scurry,
She nibbled the zwieback that she always fed off,
And when it was gone, she cut the giant's head off.

Isabel met a troublesome doctor,
He punched and he poked till he really shocked her.

The doctor's talk was of coughs and chills
And the doctor's satchel bulged with pills.
The doctor said unto Isabel,
Swallow this, it will make you well.
Isabel, Isabel, didn't worry,
Isabel didn't scream or scurry,
She took those pills from the pill concoctor,
And Isabel calmly cured the doctor.

Isabel once was asleep in bed
When a horrible dream crawled into her head.
It was worse than a dinosaur, worse than a shark,
Worse than an octopus oozing in the dark.
'Boo!' said the dream, with a dreadful grin,
'I'm going to scare you out of your skin!'
Isabel, Isabel, didn't worry,
Isabel didn't scream or scurry,
Isabel had a cleverer scheme;
She just woke up and fooled that dream.

Whenever you meet a bugaboo
Remember what Isabel used to do.
Don't scream when the bugaboo says 'Boo!'
Just look it in the eye and say, 'Boo to you!'
That's how to banish a bugaboo;
Isabel did it and so can you!
Booooo to you.

Fuzzy Wuzzy

Anonymous

/////////////////////

Fuzzy Wuzzy was a bear,

Fuzzy Wuzzy had no hair;

So Fuzzy Wuzzy

Wasn't fuzzy,

Wuzz he?

Eenie Meenie

Anonymous

I woke up Monday morning and
I looked up on the wall,
The bedbugs and mosquitoes
Were playing a game of ball.

The score was nine-to-nothing,
The mosquitoes were ahead.
The bedbugs hit a home run,
And knocked me out of bed!

Singing eenie meenie meenie-miny-mo!
You gotta catch a whippersnapper by the toe,
And if he holler hollers don't you let him go,
Singing eenie-meenie meenie-miny-mo!

Tiffy Taffy

Michael Rosen

Tiffy taffy toffee
on the flee flo floor.
Tiffy taffy toffee
on the dee doe door.
Kiffy kaffy coffee
in a jig jag jug.
Kiffy kaffy coffee
in a mig mag mug.

Wiwis

Roger McGough

To amuse
emus
on warm summer nights

Kiwis
do wiwis
from spectacular heights.

The Crocodile

Lewis Carroll

How doth the little crocodile
   Improve his shining tail,
And pour the waters of the Nile
   On every golden scale!

How cheerfully he seems to grin,
   How neatly spread his claws,
And welcomes little fishes in
   With gently smiling jaws!

Way Down South Where Bananas Grow

Anonymous

Way down south where bananas grow,
A grasshopper stepped on an elephant's toe.
The elephant said, with tears in his eyes,
'Pick on somebody your own size.'

The Grackle

Ogden Nash

The grackle's voice is less than mellow,
His heart is black, his eye is yellow,
He bullies more attractive birds
With hoodlum deeds and vulgar words,
And should a human interfere,
Attacks that human in the rear.
I cannot help but deem the grackle
An ornithological debacle.

The Blunderblat

Colin West

Until I saw the Blunderblat
I doubted its existence;
But late last night with Vera White,
I saw one in the distance.

I reached for my binoculars,
Which finally I focused;
I watched it rise into the skies,
Like some colossal locust.

I heard it hover overhead,
I shrieked as it came nearer;
I held my breath, half scared to death,
And prayed it might take Vera.

And so it did, I'm glad to say,
Without too much resistance.
Dear Blunderbat, I'm sorry that
I doubted your existence.

Hipporhinostricow

Spike Milligan

Such a beast is the Hipporhinostricow
How it got so mixed up we'll never know how;
It sleeps all day and whistles all night,
And it wears yellow socks that are far too tight.

If you laugh at the Hipporhinostricow,
You're bound to get into an awful row;
The creature is protected you see
From silly people like you and me.

The Wendigo

Ogden Nash

The Wendigo,
The Wendigo!
Its eyes are ice and indigo!
Its blood is rank and yellowish!
Its voice is hoarse and bellowish!
Its tentacles are slithery,
And scummy,
Slimy,
Leathery!
Its lips are hungry blubbery,
And smacky,
Sucky,
Rubbery!

The Wendigo,
The Wendigo!
I saw it just a friend ago!
Last night it lurked in Canada;
Tonight, on your veranada!
As you are lolling hammockwise
It contemplates you stomachwise.

You loll,
It contemplates,
It lollops.
The rest is gulps and gollops.

The Great Panjandrum

Samuel Foote

So she went into the garden
to cut a cabbage-leaf
to make an apple-pie;
and at the same time
a great she-bear, coming
   down the street,
pops its head into the shop.
What! no soap?
  So he died,
and she very imprudently married the Barber:
and there were present

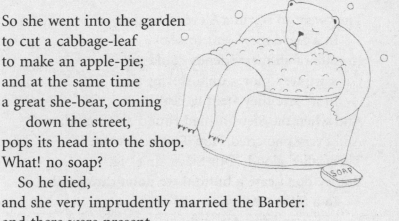

the Picninnies,
  and the Joblillies,
    and the Garyulies,
and the great Panjandrum himself,
with the little round button at top;
and they all fell to playing the game of
   catch-as-catch-can,
till the gunpowder ran out at the heels of their boots.

The Jumblies

Edward Lear

They went to sea in a Sieve, they did,
    In a Sieve they went to sea:
In spite of all their friends could say,
On a winter's morn, on a stormy day,
    In a Sieve they went to sea!
And when the Sieve turned round and round,
And every one cried, 'You'll all be drowned!'
They called aloud, 'Our Sieve ain't big,
But we don't care a button! we don't care a fig!
    In a Sieve we'll go to sea!'
      Far and few, far and few,
        Are the lands where the Jumblies live;
        Their heads are green, and their hands are blue,
        And they went to sea in a Sieve.

They sailed away in a Sieve, they did,
In a Sieve they sailed so fast,
    With only a beautiful pea-green veil
Tied with a riband by way of a sail,
    To a small tobacco-pipe mast;
And every one said, who saw them go,
'O won't they be soon upset, you know!
For the sky is dark, and the voyage is long,

And happen what may, it's extremely wrong
      In a Sieve to sail so fast!'
         Far and few, far and few,
            Are the lands where the Jumblies live;
         Their heads are green, and their hands are blue,
            And they went to sea in a Sieve.

The water it soon came in, it did,
      The water it soon came in;
So to keep them dry, they wrapped their feet
      In a pinky paper all folded neat,
And they fastened it down with a pin.
And they passed the night in a crockery-jar,
And each of them said, 'How wise we are!
Though the sky be dark, and the voyage be long,
Yet we never can think we were rash or wrong,
      While round in our Sieve we spin!'
         Far and few, far and few,
            Are the lands where the Jumblies live;
         Their heads are green, and their hands are blue,
            And they went to sea in a Sieve.

And all night long they sailed away;
      And when the sun went down,
They whistled and warbled a moony song
To the echoing sound of a coppery gong,
      In the shade of the mountains brown.
'O Timballo! How happy we are,

When we live in a Sieve and a crockery-jar,
And all night long in the moonlight pale,
We sail away with a pea-green sail,
    In the shade of the mountains brown!'
        Far and few, far and few,
           Are the lands where the Jumblies live;
        Their heads are green, and their hands are blue,
        And they went to sea in a Sieve.

They sailed to the Western Sea, they did,
  To a land all covered with trees,
And they bought an Owl, and a useful Cart,
And a pound of Rice, and a Cranberry Tart,
  And a hive of silvery Bees.
And they bought a Pig, and some green Jack-daws,
And a lovely Monkey with lollipop paws,
And forty bottles of Ring-Bo-Ree,
    And no end of Stilton Cheese.
        Far and few, far and few,
           Are the lands where the Jumblies live;
        Their heads are green, and their hands are blue,
        And they went to sea in a Sieve.

And in twenty years they all came back,
    In twenty years or more,
And every one said, 'How tall they've grown!
For they've been to the Lakes, and the Torrible Zone,
    And the hills of the Chankly Bore!'

And they drank their health, and gave them a feast
Of dumplings made of beautiful yeast;
And every one said, 'If we only live,
We too will go to sea in a Sieve, –
    To the hills of the Chankly Bore!'
        Far and few, far and few,
            Are the lands where the Jumblies live;
            Their heads are green, and their hands are blue,
            And they went to sea in a Sieve.

Jabberwocky

Lewis Carroll

'Twas brillig, and the slithy toves
    Did gyre and gimble in the wabe;
All mimsy were the borogoves,
    And the mome raths outgrabe.

'Beware the Jabberwock, my son!
    The jaws that bite, the claws that catch!
Beware the Jubjub bird, and shun
    The frumious Bandersnatch!'

He took his vorpal sword in hand:
    Long time the manxome foe he sought –
So rested he by the Tumtum tree,
    And stood awhile in thought.

And as in uffish thought he stood,
    The Jabberwock, with eyes of flame,
Came whiffling through the tulgey wood,
    And burbled as it came!

One, two! One, two! And through and through
    The vorpal blade went snicker-snack!
He left it dead, and with its head
    He went galumphing back.

'And has thou slain the Jabberwock?
    Come to my arms, my beamish boy!
O frabjous day! Callooh! Callay!'
    He chortled in his joy.

'Twas brillig, and the slithy toves
    Did gyre and gimble in the wabe;
All mimsy were the borogoves,
    And the mome raths outgrabe.

A Quadrupedremian Song

Thomas Hood

He dreamt that he saw the Buffalant,
    And the spottified Dromedaraffe,
The blue Camelotamus, lean and gaunt,
    And the wild Tigeroceros calf.

The maned Liodillo loudly roared,
    And the Peccarbok whistled its whine.
The Chinchayak leapt on the dewy sward,
    As it hunted the pale Baboonpine.

He dreamt that he met the Crocoghau,
    As it swam in the Stagnolent Lake;
But everything that in dreams he saw
    Came of eating too freely of cake.

I Saw a Peacock

Anonymous

I saw a Peacock with a fiery tail
I saw a Blazing Comet drop down hail
I saw a Cloud with Ivy circled round
I saw a sturdy Oak creep on the ground
I saw a Pismire swallow up a Whale
I saw a raging Sea brim full of Ale
I saw a Venice Glass sixteen foot deep
I saw a Well full of men's tears that weep
I saw their eyes all in a flame of fire
I saw a House as big as the Moon and higher
I saw the Sun even in the midst of night
I saw the man that saw this wondrous sight.

ACKNOWLEDGEMENTS

Every effort has been made to trace and contact all copyright holders. If there are any inadvertent omissions or errors we will be pleased to correct them at the earliest opportunity.

Vintage Classics gratefully acknowledges permission to reprint copyright material as follows:

Liz Brownlee: 'Shoem'. Copyright © Liz Brownlee 2001. Reprinted by kind permission of the author.

Charles Causley: 'There Once Was a Man'; 'I Saw a Jolly Hunter', from *I Had a Little Cat: Collected Poems for Children* (1975) by Charles Causley, published by Macmillan. Reprinted by kind permission of David Higham Associates.

Roald Dahl: 'The Centipede's Song', from *James and the Giant Peach* (1967) by Roald Dahl, published by Allen and Unwin. Reprinted by kind permission of David Higham Associates.

Julia Donaldson: 'Crazy Mayonnaisy Mum', from *Crazy Mayonnaisy Mum* by Julia Donaldson, illustrated by Nick Sharratt, published by Macmillan (2005). Copyright ©

Dandy: The Best of Ogden Nash (1994), published by Andre Deutsch. Reprinted by kind permission of Carlton Books Ltd.

Mervyn Peake: 'Of Pygmies, Palms and Pirates', from *A Book of Nonsense* (1976) by Mervyn Peake. Reprinted by kind permission of Peters Fraser & Dunlop (www.petersfraserdunlop.com) on behalf of The Estate of Mervyn Peake.

Jack Prelutsky: 'Be Glad Your Nose is on Your Face' from *Be Glad Your Nose Is On Your Face* (2008) by Jack Prelutsky; 'It's Raining Pigs and Noodles' from *It's Raining Pigs and Noodles*, text copyright © 2000 by Jack Prelutsky. Used by permission of HarperCollins Publishers.

Michael Rosen: 'Strict' from *The Hypnotiser* (1992) by Michael Rosen. Reprinted by kind permission of Peters Fraser & Dunlop (www.petersfraserdunlop.com) on behalf of Michael Rosen; 'Tiffy Taffy', from *Don't Put Mustard in the Custard* by Michael Rosen (© Michael Rosen 1981) is reprinted by kind permission of United Agents (www.unitedagents.co.uk) on behalf of Michael Rosen.

Colin West: 'The Blunderbat'. Reprinted by kind permission of the author.

Benjamin Zephaniah: 'Luv Song' by Benjamin Zephaniah (Copyright © Benjamin Zephaniah 2000) is reprinted by kind permission of United Agents (www.unitedagents.co.uk) on behalf of Benjamin Zephaniah.

The Book OF COMPLETE

NONSENSE

Find out about the different sorts of nonsense and
read Michael Rosen's tips on how to write your own!

What was all that about?

We hope you enjoyed the Vintage Children's Classics collection of nonsense verse. Writing nonsense is a time-honoured trade dating all the way back to Ancient Greece (they called it 'ambighory'). But perhaps your mind is reeling from all the mixed up words, baffling beasts and crazy ideas unleashed in these pages. If you prefer to organise your thoughts, here's a quick guide to some different types of nonsense:

Made-up words:
Lots of the poems in this collection include made-up words. Sometimes the poets have combined two or three real words to create something completely new – Liz Brownlee's 'Shoem' is a handy guide on just how this works. Can you see which animals make up Spike Milligan's Hipporhinostricow?

Sometimes the meaning of these made-up words is quite mysterious – can you guess what 'the borogoves' are in Lewis Carroll's 'Jabberwocky', or what 'slithy' means?

Edward Lear, Colin West and Edward Gorey make up words to describe fantastical creatures or places, such as the Blunderbat, the Boggerslosh or the land where the Bong Tree Grows. What do these made-up creatures look like? Why don't you draw a picture and find out?

Ridiculous rhymes:

Ogden Nash is very good at ridiculous rhymes. Look back at his poem 'The Sniffle' – if you read it out loud you'll see he's spelt words wrong in order to make them rhyme, and make you smile of course. 'There Was an Old Man Called Michael Finnigin' is another good example of this. Michael Rosen's poem 'Tiffy Taffy' is a glorious rhyme which is also very catchy!

Silly situations:

Lots of the poets imagine strange or even impossible situations and predicaments, such as raining pigs and noodles, wearing a cat or a cabbage as a hat, or noses growing between toes. Think of 'One Fine Day in the Middle of the Night', a poem full of impossible opposites.

Disgusting Dinners:

'Crazy Mayonnaisy Mum' by Julia Donaldson, and 'The Centipede's Song' by Roald Dahl are just two poems which imagine all sorts of revolting combinations of things to eat. The poets are clearly having a lot of fun coming up with these foul feasts and sick-making snacks!

Puns:

There are so many words in English which sound the same, but have a completely different meaning. Lots of jokes make use of this quirk of language, which is called a 'pun'. For instance, did you hear about the musician that robbed a bank – he ran away with the lute! Or, I used to be a doctor, but I lost patients. The poem 'Lettuce Marry' makes use of lots of these sorts of puns.

There are also lots of English words and common phrases with two or more meanings, and clever writers can use these double-meanings to comic effect. This is also called a 'pun'. A boy might 'sail through his exam with flying colours', but if that boy happened to be in the navy, this phrase has a double-meaning, and becomes funny. Here are some more pun-ny jokes:

I need to look for my missing watch, but I can never find the time.

I ate some glue but I didn't tell anyone. My lips were sealed.

I'm reading a book about anti-gravity. It's impossible to put down.

Tongue-twisters
Flick back to the poem 'A Tree Toad Loved a She-Toad' and try reading it out loud. Then try reading it out loud as fast as

you can – did your tongue get twisted? Tongue-twisters are another type of nonsense. I bet you can't say 'Unique New York' or 'red lorry yellow lorry' ten times quickly without getting in a terrible muddle! Here's another nonsense poem made up of tongue twisters:

Peter Piper picked a peck of pickled peppers.
Did Peter Piper pick a peck of pickled peppers?
If Peter Piper Picked a peck of pickled peppers,
Where is the peck of pickled peppers Peter Piper picked?

Meet Mrs Malaprop and the Reverend Spooner!

Often when we get our words mixed up or mishear things we unintentionally create nonsense words or situations and very funny results! Here are a few common sorts of real-life nonsense, and their originators:

Spoonerisms

The unfortunate Reverend Spooner (1844–1930) had a horrible habit of mixing up his words to hilarious effect. A few of the Reverend's finest moments included 'it is kisstomary to cuss the bride' (instead of 'it is customary to kiss the bride') and 'Mardon me, padom, you are occupewing my pie' (instead of 'Pardon me, madam, you are occupying my pew'). This particular type of mix-up was eventually called 'a spoonerism'.

Malapropisms

Mrs Malaprop is a character in an eighteenth-century play called *The Rivals*; she likes to use flowery vocabulary, but she often uses the wrong words, getting them mixed up with ones that sound similar. For instance she cries 'it will give me the hydrostatics' instead of 'hysterics'; or 'he is the very pineapple of politeness' instead of 'pinnacle'.

Mondegreens

Have you ever discovered you've been singing the wrong words to your favourite song? The American writer Sylvia Wright discovered she'd misheard the lyrics of an old song, so instead of the line 'laid him on the green', she had been singing 'Lady Mondegreen'! Perhaps you thought the line from the Christmas carol 'Silent Night' was 'sleep in heavenly peas'? Or that The Beatles sang 'She's got a chicken to ride'?

Test your knowledge of Nonsense

(Turn to the back for answers – no cheating!)

Have a look at the pairs of words below: can you work out which is a real word and which is complete nonsense?

1) **Serendipitous** or **Frabjous**?

2) **Platypus** or **Peccarbok**?

3) **Conboozled** or **Discombobulated**?

4) **Wendigo** or **Shoebill**?

5) **Galumphing** or **Gadhoofing**?

6) **Multitudinous** or **Manimeninous**?

7) **Chiffle** or **Skulduggery**?

8) **Sutton Woo** or **Bumbley Boo**?

9) **Spottified** or **Syllabub**?

10) **Wombat** or **Dawbis**?

Who's making up all this nonsense?

So many people have made up nonsense poems over the ages, we could only include some of their work in this anthology, and even then there are far too many poets to introduce you to – it would take all day! But here are a few word wizards you really *must* meet . . .

Anonymous

There are a lot of nonsense poems in this book by Anonymous. But, as you may know, this isn't actually one clever person with a single funny name: 'anonymous' means we don't know who wrote the poem. These poems have been chanted in nurseries and playgrounds or sung at camp for many years, and then grown-ups remember them and pass them on to their children, and so on and so on. Some of them are very old poems indeed!

Lewis Carroll

Lewis Carroll's real name was Charles Lutwidge Dodgson and he was born in 1832. He wrote *Alice's Adventures in Wonderland* and *Through the Looking Glass*. Many of the poems in this book appear in those two stories, and if you don't mind a bit of nonsense, you really should read about Alice's peculiar escapades. Lewis Carroll was very fond of puzzles, mathematical jokes and codes, and clearly enjoyed making up words, riddles and rhymes. He died on 14th January 1898.

Roald Dahl

Roald Dahl (born 1916, died 1990) wrote many wonderful and very famous books for children. Perhaps you've read *Charlie and the Chocolate Factory*? Or *Matilda*? or *Fantastic Mr Fox*? 'The Centipede's Song' is taken from *James and the Giant Peach*, which is a brilliant story about a mysteriously large peach that grows in a small boy's garden. James climbs inside it (wouldn't you?) and discovers its friendly insect inhabitants. They all roll away in the peach and have marvellous adventures together.

Edward Lear

This is a picture Edward Lear drew of himself, with his cat, Foss. Doesn't he look fun? I wish I'd known him. Unfortunately he died many years ago in 1888, but not before he'd written oodles of funny poems about

strange goings-on and imaginary creatures. There is a plentiful helping of his limericks in this collection, and his best-known poem, *The Owl and the Pussycat*.

Spike Milligan

. . . was really called Terence Alan Patrick Seán Milligan, but that's quite a mouthful, so he was known as Spike. Like Edward Lear, Spike was also a musician, playing the trumpet and singing in jazz bands. Mainly he was known for his part in a comical radio show which broadcast in the 1940s and '50s, called *The Goon Show*, to which he contributed lots of puns, jokes and silly sound effects. His nonsense poetry has always been very popular – 'On the Ning Nang Nong' was voted the UK's favourite comic poem in 1998.

Ogden Nash

Ogden Nash was an American poet who also wrote a lot of nonsense, in fact, the *New York Times* said he was the best nonsense poet in the country and he even appeared on a US postage stamp! He was very good at puns and rhyming – he once said he even thought in rhyme! – and he often invented or deliberately misspelled words in order to create funny rhymes. He wrote several poems about his daughter Isabel, and we've included a couple of them in this collection. Don't you wish someone might write a funny poem about you?

Michael Rosen

If you've never read any of Michael Rosen's poems, except for the ones in this collection, I think you should run off to a library or bookshop and find some right now! You won't regret it. Michael Rosen was born in 1946 and both his parents were teachers who loved to tell stories and jokes and sing songs. He once worked for the BBC creating children's programmes for radio and television, but nowadays he mostly writes books and poems (a lot of them about his own child-hood and family) and goes into schools to help children to write poems, and to perform some of his own. He is awfully good at reading his poems, and if you go to his website (www. michaelrosen.co.uk) you'll see for yourself. Read on to find out what Michael thinks about nonsense poetry . . .

Michael Rosen Answers Some Questions About Nonsense

1) What is 'nonsense' poetry then?

Nonsense poetry is a way of making new language. It's not non-sense. It's *new* sense. Words, phrases, creatures, plants, landscapes, scenes and time itself can be changed. Some people say that nonsense is 'no rules'. Again, I think it's new rules. Or new-ish. You take the old rules – whatever they are, and alter them. Most nonsense poetry in English likes to follow the sound and feel of traditional poetry. Perhaps that's in order to make the contrast between the new-sense and the known world, all the more surprising.

2) Can anyone write it, or is it just by poets?

Of course anyone can write it and very young people do it all the time. We all like to take the familiar sounds, words and ideas and play with them: spoonerisms, backslang, mock alphabets, tongue-twisters, limericks, nicknames – we do these things all the time.

3) It's all crazy made-up words and loopy rhymes – what's the point of nonsense verse?

We may never know the point. It may not have a point. We may not need a point. We get points all the time. We can't get away from people making points. Perhaps nonsense poetry is a time when there isn't a point. And that's the point.

4) OK, so I want to make up my own nonsense – where do I start?

You could start with your name, someone else's name, the name of an animal or plant or building. You could play with that name, mix it with another. This thing or person or creature needs something or lacks something or has a problem. This need or lack might be familiar like hunger or love or danger or loss but the way this thing or creature or being is going to solve this problem is going to be strange: a strange meeting? a strange landscape? a strange passing of time? And maybe this won't solve the problem. And if not, it may not matter. We might be left hanging in the air. Like a doughnut.

5) Do you eat your peas with honey?

I eat my bees with honey. Peas don't sting.

Nonsensical Things to Do

Play Consequences!

Take turns to make up a story with your friends – the game is to each write a line of the story without knowing what the other players have written!

What you'll need

   Pens

   Paper

   At least two people

Each player takes a piece of paper. Write a line of the story and then fold down the paper so what you've just written is concealed, but leave enough blank paper for the next line of the story. Then pass your paper to the next player. Continue writing a line, folding, and passing the paper on until you've finished the story on each player's paper.

You can write whatever you like, but it might help to stick to this sort of structure:

A boy/girl/animal called _____ (you could use your friend's name!)

Met a boy/girl/animal called _____

In/At/On_____ (think of an unusual or unlikely place, perhaps the planet Mars, or the back of the number 7 bus).

He/She said_____.

She/He replied_____.

Then he/she _____(did, said something, went some-where).

So she/he_____.

And the consequences were_____(e.g. they lived happily ever after).

When you've reached the end of the story, unfold your paper and take turns to read the ridiculous story out loud!

Play Picture Consequences!
This is a similar game to the one above, but instead of words you each draw part of a monster, folding down the paper to hide your drawing and then passing the paper on to the next player. First draw the head, then the shoulders and arms, then the torso and hips, then the legs, then the feet. Make sure you leave a bit of neck, body and legs visible so the next

player can draw in the right place. At the end, unfold the paper and see what sort of crazy monster you've created! Give it a name, and perhaps even write a nonsense poem about it!

Tell Us a Story!

This is a great game for family car journeys and it's very simple to play. You make up a story one word at a time, each player taking turns to add a word. The trick is to keep the story moving as fast as possible – no long pauses allowed! – but try and work together to create a funny and exciting tale!

Answers to the Nonsense Quiz – how did you do?

1) **Serendipitous** means lucky, or found by happy accident. **Frabjous** is nonsense, from Lewis Carroll's poem 'Jabberwocky'.

2) A **Platypus** is a strange-looking semi-aquatic mammal. A **Peccarbok** is a nonsense creature from Thomas Hood's poem 'A Quadrupedremian Song'.

3) **Conboozled** is nonsense from Liz Brownlee's poem 'Shoem'. **Discombobulated** means very confused.

4) The **Wendigo** is a nonsense creature from Ogden Nash's poem of the same name. A **Shoebill** is a kind of large bird with a shoe-shaped beak that lives in Africa.

5) **Galumphing** was nonsense when Lewis Carroll made it up in 'Jabberwocky', but it has since become a real world and now you'll find it in the dictionary, meaning to run clumsily or heavily. **Gadhoofing** is nonsense.

6) **Multitudinous** means made up of many parts. **Manimeninous** is nonsense.

7) **Chiffle** is nonsense from Ogden Nash's poem 'The Sniffle' (it's really 'cheerful', spelt wrong). **Skulduggery** means trickery, lies and other bad behaviour.

8) **Sutton Hoo** is a real location in Suffolk. **Bumbley Boo** is nonsense from Spike Milligan's poem, 'The Land of the Bumbley Boo'.

9) **Spottified** is nonsense from Thomas Hood's poem 'A Quadrupedremian Song'. **Syllabub** is a kind of milky or creamy dessert.

10) A **Wombat** is an Australian mammal that mainly comes out at night. A **Dawbis** is a nonsense creature from Edward Gorey's 'Utter Zoo Alphabet'.

Visit www.worldofstories.co.uk